THE STEM CELL THEORY OF RENEWAL
Demystifying the Most Dramatic Scientific Breakthrough of Our Time

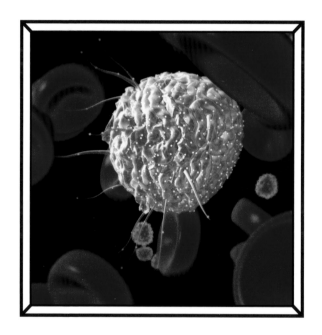

CHRISTIAN DRAPEAU, MSc.

sutton hart press
PORTLAND, OREGON

SUTTON HART PRESS

www.suttonhart.com

PRODUCED AND PRINTED IN THE UNITED STATES OF AMERICA
ISBN: 978-0-9815027-9-3

Book Design: M. Warren

Table of Contents

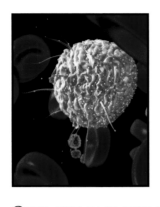

Preface

OVER THE PAST FEW YEARS THE WORLD HAS SEEN AN unprecedented explosion in the field of stem cell research. Hardly a week passes by without an article in one of the main printed newspapers, describing a new breakthrough involving stem cells. Stem cell research is arguably today one of the most prolific fields of science. And yet, very little of the available information has reached the general population – or even the health profession – in a manner that allows people to clearly understand the basics as well as the tremendous promise of stem cell research.

A short publication like this one certainly cannot provide a comprehensive account of stem cell research nor can it do justice to such important advances in health science. Yet, I hope that it can provide the reader with enough information to get a glimpse of the new frontiers opened by stem cell research. Understanding the role of stem cells in the body will give rise to a new health paradigm.

This short book is intended to describe the basics of stem cell research, focusing on the fact that stem cells constitute the natural renewal system of the body and on the concept that the number of stem cells circulating in the bloodstream is one of the greatest indicators

1

of human health. More stem cells circulating in the blood equates to greater health. With this in mind, we describe here the discovery of the first stem cell enhancer.

At times technical terms may be used for which there are no accurate simpler synonyms. In such cases, the term has been italicized and a definition can be found in the glossary at the end of the book.

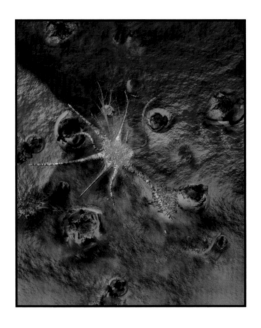

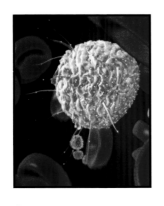

WHAT IS
A STEM CELL?

STEM CELLS ARE DEFINED AS CELLS WITH THE UNIQUE capacity to self-replicate throughout the entire life of an organism and to *differentiate* into cells of various tissues. Most cells of the body are specialized and play a well-defined role in the body. For example, brain cells respond to electrical signals from other brain cells and release neurotransmitters, cells of the retina are activated by light and pancreatic ß-cells produce insulin. These cells, called somatic cells, will never differentiate into other types of cells or even proliferate. By contrast, stem cells are primitive cells that remain undifferentiated until they receive a signal prompting them to become various types of specialized cells.

Generally speaking, there are two types of stem cells: embryonic stem cells and adult stem cells. Embryonic stem cells are cells extracted from the *blastula*, the very early embryo, while adult stem cells are stem cells found in the body after birth. The term "adult stem cells" does not refer to a characteristic associated with adulthood, but rather a contrast with the developing embryo. Stem cells in the bone marrow of a newborn baby, for example, or even stem cells found in the umbilical cord are referred to as adult stem cells.

3

EMBRYONIC STEM CELLS (ESC)

Embryonic stem cells (ESC) are derived from the inner cell mass of the blastula, the very early embryo. ECS are said to be pluripotent, meaning that they can become virtually any type of cell, which is obvious since from these cells will develop an entire human being. In nature, ESC are very short-lived as they only exist in the early embryo. As ESC develop and commit themselves to becoming the various cell types of the developing fetus, they gradually lose their pluripotency. When cultured in vitro, however, ESC can be maintained and can proliferate almost eternally.

Although ESC have been studied for a long time as part of the study of embryonic development, it is only since 1998 that human ESC have been successfully grown in vitro. The successful culture of human ESC immediately spurred a series of questions:

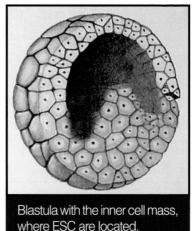

Blastula with the inner cell mass, where ESC are located.

- Since ESC can become virtually any cell type of the body, could injection of ESC lead to significant health improvements?
- Would it be possible to grow organs in vitro for the purpose of transplant?
- Could we manipulate the genetic material of embryonic stem cells in order to repair faulty genes in an organ?

Over the years, the following criteria have been developed to scientifically define an ESC:

Immortality and telomerase activity. Telomerase is an enzyme involved in cellular division. The disappearance of telomerase activity has been linked to the *senescence* of a cell. And vice versa, the immortality of a cell has been associated with high telomerase activity. Therefore, ESC are characterized by high telomerase activity and immortality.

Pluripotency. Pluripotency is the ability to become any cell type of the body, except germ cells (egg and spermatogonia). Many protocols have been developed to trigger the differentiation of ESC into virtually any cell type of the body.

Maintenance of its properties after numerous generations. One criterion for the "stemness" of a cell is its ability to divide numerous times while retaining its *integrity*. As a stem cell divides, at one point, after a number of generations, it will begin to differentiate into other types of cells. An ESC maintains its "stemness" after numerous generations.

Ability to contribute to the formation of a *teratoma*. The injection of ESC isolated from the blastula in an animal will lead to the development of a teratoma, a cancerous cell mass containing fragments of several organs and tissues of the body. The formation of a teratoma demonstrates two things: a) the cell has an enormous ability to multiply, and b) it can become any cell type of the body. This became a golden test to determine whether a cell is a stem cell, as only stem cells will have the ability to multiply and become various parts of the body.

But such discussions and efforts became rapidly encumbered by profound ethical and moral considerations. Since the source of human ESC has to be human embryos, central to this issue is the main question, deeply buried into religions: "When is an embryo considered a full human being?" The idea of growing human embryos for the sole purpose of extracting ESC is obviously questionable. Many people believe that the fertilized egg, having the potential of becoming a full human being, is already a legal person. Therefore, based on this view, the use of ESC is akin to murder. On the other hand, supporters of ESC research argue that an embryo is far from a full human being, and if using embryos can save lives and increase quality of life then it is worth it. After all, argue supporters of ESC research, these embryos are unused fertilized eggs coming from fertility clinics and they are going to be disposed of anyway, so why not use them for saving lives instead of simply discarding them? Thus far this debate has greatly restricted the development of ESC research.

But aside from such ethical and moral considerations, the main issue is that in spite of all the promises of ESC research, nearly 10 years of research have not delivered one successful and safe ESC-based therapeutic approach. Many studies using ESC have shown that although results can at times be remarkable, there is a significant risk of developing tumors.

SCIENTIFIC BIAS AGAINST ADULT STEM CELLS
The manner with which stem cells have been defined has created a significant bias that has hindered the development of adult stem cell research for a long time.

As stated previously, through the course of scientific investigations, ESC became defined as cells having the ability to grow many generations in vitro, to maintain their integrity after many generations, and to become cells of virtually any tissue of the body.

Initially this concept was meant to define all stem cells in general. However, when applied to adult stem cells (ASC), it was found that:

- they are very difficult to grow in vitro,
- they do not maintain their integrity after many generations in vitro,
- they do not differentiate easily in vitro,
- and injection of ASC under the skin does not lead to the formation of a teratoma.

Therefore, for a long time ASC were considered lesser stem cells with very little capability and therapeutic potential. ASC certainly showed some level of "stemness", as evidenced by the ability of *hematopoietic* stem cells or blood adult stem cells to become red blood cells, lymphocytes and platelets, but the belief that they were limited in their ability to become other types of cells led to a general lack of investigation of their therapeutic potential. They were simply considered lesser stem cells.

A second research bias came from the very fact that it is difficult to grow ASC in vitro. When growing embryonic stem cells, entire *cell lines* can be developed from one single cell and research can be done in a controlled manner with billions of identical cells. But since ACS cannot be easily grown in vitro, it is much more difficult to work with ASC in a controlled manner.

As a consequence ASC have been studied much less, leaving a significant gap in the literature between ESC and ASC.

However, the potential of ASC has been clearly revealed over the past 5 years thanks to the work of numerous scientific teams throughout the world. A large body of scientific data indicates that ASC have capabilities comparable to ESC when studied in a living organism as opposed to a test tube. For example, an ASC exposed to brain tissue will rapidly become a neuron or a *glial cell*,[1,2] when exposed to liver tissue ASC will rapidly become liver cells,[3,4] and hair follicle stem cells can regenerate a sectioned spinal cord.[5] In short, ASC can virtually become every cell type of the body, opening an entirely new path of research in the field of health and wellness.[6,7,8,9,10,11]

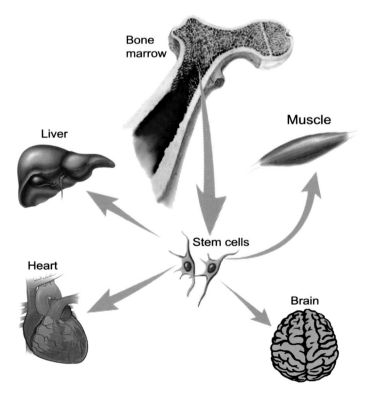

Bone marrow

Muscle

Liver

Stem cells

Heart

Brain

THE POTENTIAL OF ADULT STEM CELLS

Today we know that ASC are undifferentiated or primitive cells that can self-renew and can differentiate into specialized cells of various tissues. Though ASC are most predominantly found in the bone marrow, they can also be isolated from various tissues such as the liver,[12] the intestine,[13] muscles,[14] the brain,[15] the pancreas,[16] as well as blood and many other tissues.[17]

The role of ASC found in tissues is to maintain and repair the tissue in which they are found, though local stem cells appear to be involved only in relatively minor repair of the tissue in which they reside. In case of major injury or degeneration, the need for stem cells far exceeds the number of stem cells available in the tissue, and stem cells from the bone marrow (BMSC) are called to contribute to the repair process.

BMSC have traditionally been considered to have little potential for *plasticity*, being limited in their development to red blood cells, lymphocytes, platelets, bone and connective tissue. However much scientific work has been published over the past few years demonstrating the exceptional plasticity of BMSC. After transplantation, bone marrow and enriched hematopoietic stem cells (HSC) were shown to have the ability to become muscle cells,[18] heart cells,[19] endothelium capillary cells,[20] liver cells,[3] lung,[21] gut [21] and skin cells,[22] as well as neural cells.[23]

Jang et al[3] performed an elegant experiment in which stem cells were co-cultured with either normal or damaged liver tissue. The stem cells and liver tissue were separated by a *semi-permeable membrane* with pores large enough to let molecules pass through but small enough to prevent the passage of cells from one

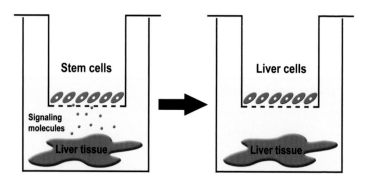

Stem cells

Liver cells

Signaling molecules

Liver tissue

Liver tissue

When stem cells are placed in a semi-permeable well with pores large enough to let molecules pass through but small enough to prevent the passage of cells, exposure to damaged liver tissue leads to the transformation of the stem cells into liver cells. Molecules secreted by the injured tissue, which are specific for that tissue, reach the stem cells and trigger the process of differentiation. Differentiation of a stem cell into a specific cell type is triggered by contact with molecules specific to that tissue.

compartment to the other (pore size 0.4 µm). Using markers for both the stem cells and livers cells, the authors documented that when stem cells were placed in the presence of damaged liver tissue, they rapidly adopted characteristics of liver cells. Within eight hours after being put in contact with damaged liver tissue, the stem cells had begun their conversion into liver cells.

BONE MARROW AND STEM CELLS

Many think that the bone is a solid structure with very little blood circulation – basically nothing more than a lifeless deposit of calcium. This is hardly the case. Bones are very much alive, with significant blood circulation. Given the importance of the bone marrow as the source of stem cells, it is pertinent to briefly describe what the bone marrow is.

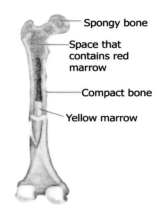

There are two types of bone structure: compact and spongy. These two bone structures differ in density and in how tightly the bone tissue is organized. The strength of a bone comes from the amount and density of compact bone.

Bone marrow morphology

The blood circulation and the "life" of a bone are found in the spongy bone. This is where the bone marrow is located – in small cavities within the spongy bone.

In children, the bones contain only red marrow. However, as the skeleton matures, fat-storing yellow marrow displaces red marrow in the shafts of the long bones of the limbs. In adults, red marrow remains chiefly in the ribs, the vertebrae, the pelvic bones, and the skull. It is in the red marrow that stem cells are produced, so the transformation of red marrow into yellow marrow explains the decline in stem cell production with age. The frequency of stem cells in the bone marrow has been estimated to be about 1 in 10,000 marrow cells, for an estimate total of approximately 150 million stem cells.

In general, cells divide in nature through a process referred to as "symmetrical division" whereby the mother cell divides into two identical daughter cells. During this process a copy of the mother cell's DNA is made.

As shown in the diagram below, one strand of the original DNA (green) and one strand of its copy (red) go into each daughter cell. In the bone marrow however, cellular division takes place through a process referred to as "asymmetrical division" whereby the two daughter cells are not identical. One daughter inherits the copies of the DNA while the other one retains the original DNA. The former is called to leave the bone marrow while the latter remains in the bone marrow, keeping the original DNA as the blueprint for future cells. Therefore, through this process, despite of the release of stem cells from the bone marrow, the number of stem cells always remains relatively constant in the bone marrow. This process is also referred to as the "immortal strand hypothesis".[24] Therefore supporting the release of stem cells from the bone marrow will not deplete or affect the bone marrow.

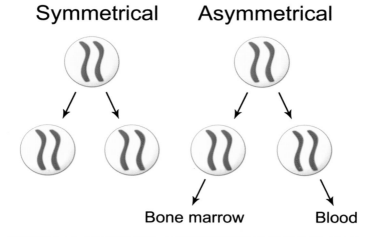

Symmetrical   Asymmetrical

Bone marrow   Blood

Asymmetrical cellular division is a process taking place in the bone marrow whereby the original DNA gets segregated into one daughter cell that remains in the bone marrow while the other cell containing a copy of the DNA is released in the bloodstream. This process preserves the original DNA in the bone marrow throughout the life of an individual.

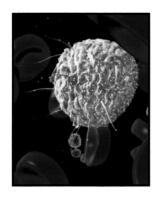

THE STEM CELL THEORY OF RENEWAL

MORE ON ADULT STEM CELLS

As mentioned previously, ASC are well known for their role in the constant renewal of blood cells (red blood cells, lymphocytes and platelets) and the regeneration of bone, ligament, tendon and connective tissues. But until recently it was believed that this was the extent of their ability to become other types of cell.

So how was the true role of stem cells in the body discovered? How is it that with today's level of scientific sophistication, we only recently discovered this phenomenon? For if we think about it carefully, such a discovery amounts to nothing less than the discovery of a whole new system in the body!

A system is a tissue or organ or a set of tissues and organs comprised of specific cells that accomplish specific tasks affecting other organs and tissues, aimed at supporting the health and survival of the whole organism. For example, the cardiovascular system is comprised of the heart and its task is to pump blood in order to deliver nutrients and oxygen to every cell of the body. The digestive system is comprised of the stomach and intestine and its task is to digest food into absorbable nutrients in order to feed every cell of the body. The endocrine system is comprised of severalorgans whose task is to secrete compounds called hormones that modulate the functioning of other organs and tissues. For example, the pancreas secretes insulin that allows the transport of glucose into cells, and the thyroid gland secretes thyroid hormones that stimulate body metabolism. Regarding stem cells, we have the bone marrow that secretes cells that travel and migrate into damaged tissues, restoring optimal functioning. Science has discovered the renewal system of the body!

How can such a discovery have waited so long to be made? We can

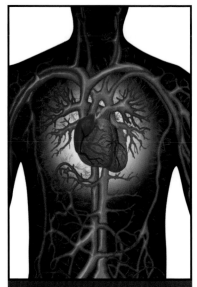

The cardiovascular system is composed of the heart and all the blood vessels carrying the blood to the tissues and then back to the heart. The cardiovascular system allows for the distribution of oxygen and nutrients to every cell of the body.

find the answer in the history of science itself, where oftentimes breakthrough discoveries are only made once the necessary tools are developed. For example, how did we discover bacteria? After the development of the microscope. The microscope was originally developed to count thread density in fabrics. One day, pushed by curiosity, Antonie van Leeuwenhoek used his microscope to look at a drop of water and described for the first time tiny microorganisms moving in the water. Bacteria were observed for the first time... and not only were bacteria thus discovered, but we soon realized that bacteria are everywhere to be found.

The discovery of the role of stem cells in the body follows the same storyline. A spontaneously fluorescent protein called green *fluorescent protein* (GFP) was isolated from the deep ocean jellyfish *Aequoria victoria*. Since GFP is a protein, it is possible to derive the DNA responsible for its production and to incorporate the GFP-gene in the nucleus of a stem cell. In such case, all the cells derived from the original fluorescent stem cell will be fluorescent. The discovery of GFP is of such importance that it was actually awarded the 2008 Nobel Prize in chemistry.

When scientist began injecting fluorescent stem cells in irradiated animals –a treatment that kills all stem cells in the body–, soon thereafter fluorescent tissue cells began to appear in various tissues. But more important, if an injury was applied to any specific tissue, the area of the injury would soon begin to display significant amounts of fluorescence. The injured area was being filled with new functional specialized cells of that tissue, but the cells were fluorescent, indicating that they came from the bone marrow. A process that until then had been virtually invisible suddenly became visible – a discovery that is changing the very way in which we view biological science!

Thanks to the discovery of GFP, adult stem cells from the bone marrow have been shown to have the ability to naturally become, in the body, cells of the liver, muscle, retina, kidney, pancreas, lung, skin and even the brain ... putting an end to the dogma that we are born with a set number of brain cells and that the brain cannot regenerate. But the most fascinating observation emerging from these studies is that this process is natural. After an injury or a simple stress in an organ, bone marrow stem cells travel to that organ and play a crucial role in the process of tissue repair.

THE STEM CELL THEORY OF RENEWAL

Have you ever wondered what happens when you scratch or burn your skin, or break a bone? How does the

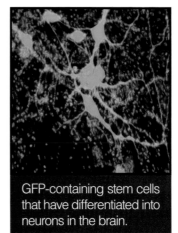

GFP-containing stem cells that have differentiated into neurons in the brain.

body repair itself? The conventional view is that skin cells called fibroblasts create an extracellular matrix made of *collagen,* on which epithelial cells proliferate and migrate to reconstitute the damaged tissue. Although this process appears to explain the phenomenon of repair in small superficial injuries, it cannot account for the repair of more significant tissue damage. First, *epithelial cells* do not have the ability to differentiate into all the various cell types involved in the repair of complex tissues. For example, when considering skin repair, the newly formed skin will contain hair follicles, sebaceous glands, and sweat glands, and epithelial cells do not have the ability to become such cells. And second, epithelial cells or other cell types generally do not proliferate at a rate that can account for the rapid repair process taking place in various tissues.

What has emerged over the past few years, through a vast body of scientific literature, is the novel view that the process of repair and renewal taking place in the body involves bone marrow stem cells. In brief, when a tissue is subjected to significant stress, stem cells originating from the bone marrow migrate to the tissue, proliferate and differentiate into cells of that tissue, thereby supporting the repair process.[25] This natural process of repair has been described in many tissues and organs of the body. It is the natural process of tissue renewal taking place in the body every day of our lives, from the day we are born!

Let's briefly describe the process that takes place any time a tissue is exposed to stress and needs assistance. A few hours after an instance of tissue stress or damage, the affected tissue releases a compound called *Granulocyte Colony-Stimulating Factor* (G-CSF). G-CSF is well known to trigger stem cell release from the bone marrow.[26] G-CSF is routinely used prior to cancer treatments involving chemotherapy or radiation. Since such treatments are known to kill all stem cells in the body, requiring stem cell transplantation after the treatment, G-CSF is commonly injected into the cancer patient to trigger stem cell release from the bone marrow in order to harvest and *cryo-preserve* stem cells. After the treatment, the stem cells are thawed and re-injected in the patient to reconstitute the bone marrow.

After tissue damage, as its concentration slowly and naturally increases in the blood, G-CSF triggers the release of stem cells from the bone marrow, increasing the number of stem cells circulating in the blood.[26]

As we will see below, much scientific evidence indicates that this aspect is probably the most crucial part of the whole process. Increasing the number of circulating stem cells means that more stem cells are available to migrate in the damaged tissue.

Soon afterward, the affected tissue releases a unique compound called *Stromal-Derived Factor-1* (SDF-1).[27]

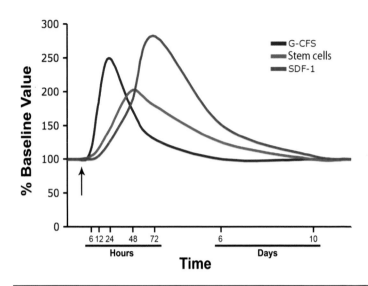

Within a few hours after an instance of tissue damage, G-CSF appears in the bloodstream. G-CSF triggers the release of stem cells whose numbers increase in the blood over the next few days. Within 24 hours after the incident, the affected tissue begins secreting SDF-1, which peaks at 72 hours. SDF-1 is the only compound known to attract stem cells.

SDF-1 is the only compound known to attract stem cells. When SDF-1 binds to *CXCR4*, the receptor present on the surface of stem cells, this binding process triggers the expression of *adhesion molecules* on the surface of the cell. Therefore, as SDF-1 diffuses from the affected area to the blood circulation and as stem cells circulating in the blood travel through the affected tissue, the binding of SDF-1 to CXCR4 triggers the adhesion of stem cells to the capillary wall and subsequently their migration into the tissue.[28] When they arrive in the target tissue, stem cells proliferate and then differentiate into cells of that tissue, thereby assisting in the repair of the tissue.[29]

This whole process has now been demonstrated in numerous studies and stem cells have been shown to participate to the repair of muscles, bone, pancreas, brain, skin, liver, intestine, lung ... virtually every organ and tissue of the body![17]

In this whole process, the number of stem cells circulating in the bloodstream appears to be the most important factor. When the level of circulating stem cells was measured in the bloodstream of individuals who suffered an injury, the individuals who had the largest number of stem cells on the day of their injury showed the fastest and greatest recovery.[30]

Likewise, when the number of stem cells was quantified in the bloodstream of nearly 500 individuals

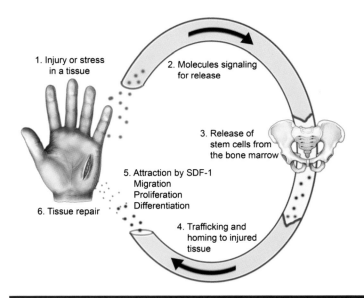

This diagram adapted from Reference 29 depicts the various steps of the process by which BMSC are released form the BM and migrate to tissues in need. First, the stressed tissue releases G-CSF that travels to the BM and triggers the release of stem cells. Then the stressed tissue releases SDF-1 and as stem cells circulate through the stressed tissue, they are attracted by SDF-1. Following the SDF-1, stem cells migrate in the tissue, proliferate and differentiate to become cells of that tissue.

and their health condition was monitored for one year, the individuals with a larger number of stem cells in their blood showed a greater level of health.[31] In other words, more stem cells circulating in the bloodstream means more stem cells available to migrate into tissues that might need assistance.

SAFE DAILY STEM CELL SUPPORT:
A NOVEL APPROACH TO WELLNESS

These discoveries have allowed a remarkable light to be shed on a little known aquabotanical called *Aphanizomenon flos-aquae* (AFA). AFA has been in the marketplace for nearly 3 decades and people consuming it have reported a wide variety of health benefits. These benefits were initially classified into three broad categories:

- benefits on the immune system,
- support of a healthy inflammatory process,
- and benefits on the nervous system. Over the years, specific compounds were identified in AFA that partially explained the reported benefits.[32]

But throughout the years people also reported a wide range of health benefits touching various aspects of human physiology that could not be fully explained by the presence of these compounds. How one single botanical product could produce so many benefits remained a mystery for many years, until the recent discovery that AFA contains a compound called an L-selectin ligand that supports stem cell release from the bone marrow.

L-selectin is an adhesion molecule that plays a critical role in the maintenance of stem cells in the bone marrow.[40] Blocking L-selectin increases the probability that a stem cell gets released from the bone marrow.[41] A team of scientists has developed a proprietary 5:1

AFA contains a *polysaccharide* that supports the activation of a specific type of lymphocyte called *natural killer (NK) cells*,[33] as well as their migration out of the blood into tissues.[34] It is in the tissues that NK cells can carry out their specific task of scavenging and killing dysfunctional cells. AFA was also shown to stimulate *macrophage* activity, macrophages being the first line of defense of the human body.[32]

AFA contains a blue pigment called phycocyanin. In the living AFA cell, phycocyanin acts as a powerful antioxidant.[35] But aside from its antioxidant properties, phycocyanin strongly supports a healthy inflammatory process.[36,37]

AFA contains a unique compound called phenyl-ethylamine (PEA). PEA is a natural compound produced by the brain when one is in love or content; in chemistry it is called the "molecule of love". A deficiency in PEA has been associated with poor concentration, low mood and even at times depression, and oral consumption of PEA has been shown to alleviate these conditions.[38,39] The most common benefit reported by people consuming AFA is an increase in mental energy and clarity. Oral intake of PEA may also support a healthier sleep pattern.

concentrate of AFA that concentrates the L-selectin ligand. Feeding one gram of this AFA concentrate to individuals was shown to increase the number of circulating stem cells by 25-30%, adding approximately 2-4 million new stem cells to the bloodstream.[42] While supporting the natural renewal system, such increase is well within normal physiological range of the body and presents no risk for the body.

This AFA concentrate is the first natural stem cell enhancer available in the marketplace. By supporting the release of stem cells from the bone marrow, it provides for mild and safe daily support of stem cell physiology. Supporting stem cell physiology is a new paradigm in health and wellness, and much scientific

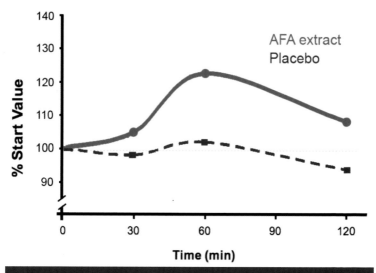

In a double-blind crossover placebo controlled study, consumption of 1 gram of an AFA extract concentrating the L-selectin ligand led to an increase of an average of 25-30% in the number of circulating stem cells, providing for an increase of 2-4 million new stem cells in the bloodstream. This increase peaked around 60 minutes after consumption and lasted 3-4 hours.

evidence indicates that this may very well be the best strategy to assist the body in maintaining optimal health.

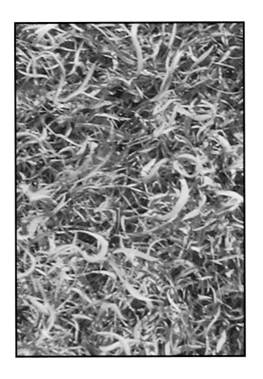

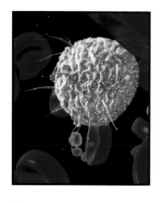

STEM CELLS
AND HEALTH

THE DISCOVERY THAT INCREASING THE NUMBER OF circulating stem cells equates to greater health, coupled with the discovery of a natural compound that supports the release of stem cells from the bone marrow, offers a new strategy in the pursuit of health and wellness. In theory, since BMSC have the ability of becoming virtually any cells of the body, supporting stem cell release has the potential of supporting all aspects of human health. BMSC have been shown to support the health of the nervous system,[43,44,45,46,47] cardiac function,[48,49,50] liver function,[51] pancreatic function,[52,53,54] kidney function,[55,56] as well as lung,[57,58] skin,[59,60] and bone health.[61,62] In essence the discovery of the role of stem cells in the body leads to a broader understanding of how the body takes care of itself, opening up exciting avenues in our quest for optimal health.

A NEW PARADIGM

The discovery that BMSC constitute the natural renewal system of the body has paved the way to a new paradigm in health and wellness. Once we understand that every day of our lives the role of stem cells is to patrol the body and migrate into areas needing assistance, then we realize that supporting stem cell physiology is the best strategy to maintain optimal health. Health problems do not begin the day we receive a diagnosis or the day we suddenly decide that we have had enough, that quality of life has decreased to a level we are no longer willing to accept, at which point we decide to go and see the doctor... health problems begin to develop years if not decades before we experience the real problem.

For example, 10 years ago John used to climb stairs 3 steps at a time. Then 5 years ago John slowly decreased to 2 steps at a time, which is still good. But then 2 years ago he began climbing stairs one step at a time and soon after that he began stopping in the middle of a staircase to catch his breath. This steady decline experienced by many people is considered to be the natural process of aging. It is the slow degradation of cardiac functions, and the same process takes place in virtually all tissues of the body. But already in the early days of this process the affected tissue releases compounds that attract stem cells, allowing the natural process of renewal to take place. Supporting the release of stem cells from the bone marrow and increasing the number of circulating stem cells in the early stages of this natural process thus supports the ability of the body to maintain optimal health.

As mentioned previously, the number of stem cells circulating in the bloodstream has been shown to be a determinant factor for overall health. More stem cells circulating in the blood equates to greater health, as more stem cells are available for the day-to-day natural process of repair in the whole body.

Therefore the discovery of the natural renewal system of the body, along with the discovery of a natural product that supports stem cell release, both open the door to a novel way of looking at health. Instead of looking at health as an absence of illness and at any health-promoting strategy as a way to postpone illnesses, we can begin to look at health as a natural process, an intrinsic ability of the body. The human body possesses the natural ability to remain healthy, and supporting this natural ability by increasing the number of circulating stem cells is logically the best way to enjoy optimal health.

And beyond the concept of optimal health is the concept of performance, or simply getting more out of our bodies than simply meeting the demands of daily life. From hiking in the mountains on weekends and a sporadic bike rides or walk, to competing in a triathlon, any physical activity beyond normal daily movements creates small injuries in muscles. Increasing the number of circulating stem cells supports the natural repair of muscle tissue, allowing for a more enjoyable experience when biting into life.

Many compounds are being studied with great promise for their ability to support stem cell physiology. But so far the only natural product that was scientifically shown to support stem cell release from the bone marrow is a patented proprietary AFA extract.[42] This product has been in the marketplace for three years and numerous reports by consumers back the theory that supporting stem cell release is probably the best strategy to maintain optimal health. As stem cells possess the ability to become virtually any kind of cell in the body, supporting stem cell release can potentially enhance the health of every organ and tissue of the body, offering a golden opportunity for ongoing health and wellness to virtually everyone.

With stem cell enhancers now becoming a whole new category of nutritional supplement, much like antioxidants in the 1990s, people looking for the latest breakthroughs in wellness will be well served to learn more about the amazing potential of stem cell nutrition.

GLOSSARY

Adhesion molecule: Proteins located on the surface of cells that allow them to bind with other cells or with the extracellular matrix. When talking about stem cells, adhesion molecules play a crucial role in the migration of stem cells across capillaries.

Aphanizomenon flos-aquae: A species of blue-green algae growing with exceptional abundance in Klamath Lake, in Southern Oregon.

Blastula: An early stage of embryonic development in mammals. It consists of a spherical layer of around 128 cells.

Collagen: The main protein of connective tissue and the most abundant protein in mammals, making up about 50% of the whole-body protein content. Collagen forms the major structure or "skeleton" of organs and tissues. It is responsible for skin strength and elasticity.

Committed stem cell: Stem cell that possesses specific markers indicating that it has committed itself to becoming a specific type of cell. For example, a stem cell containing albumin is thought to be committed to become a liver cell.

Cryo-preservation: The science or method of preserving a live cell, tissue or organism through controlled freezing.

CXCR4: A receptor at the surface of stem cells and other immune cells that is specific for a compound called stromal-derived factor 1 (SDF-1). Binding of SDF-1 to CXCR4 leads to the expression of adhesion molecules.

Differentiation: Cellular differentiation is the process by which a less specialized cell becomes a more specialized cell type. In this book, it refers to the process by which a stem cell becomes a specialized cell of a tissue.

Embryonic stem cell (ESC) line: A culture of ESC, extracted from the blastula, that appear genetically normal and have proliferated in cell culture for several months without differentiating.

Epithelial cells: Cells making up the epithelium, which is a tissue that lines the cavities and surfaces of structures throughout the body, such as the stomach, intestines, and blood vessels.

Glial cell: Commonly called neuroglia or simply glia (Greek for "glue"), glial cells are non-neuronal cells that form the so-called white matter in the brain. While they are traditionally known to provide support and nutrition to neurons, recent studies have revealed that they may play a much more important role in overall brain function.

Granulocyte Colony-Stimulating Factor (G-CSF): A glycoprotein produced by various tissues of the body that stimulates the bone marrow to release stem cells into the blood.

Hematopoietic: Linked to the term "hematopoiesis" that comes from Ancient Greek (*haima* = blood and *poiesis* = to make) and which refers to the formation of blood cells. All blood cells are derived from hematopoietic stem cells.

Integrity: When referring to stem cells, integrity refers to the characteristic of a stem cell that has retained its pluripotency. In other words, it has not differentiated.

Macrophage: From Ancient Greek (*makros* = large and *phagein* = eat), macrophages are immune cells that help initiate an immune response. Their role is to engulf and digest cellular debris and pathogens during an infection.

Natural killer (NK) cells: A type of lymphocyte (blood cell) that plays a major role in the elimination of tumors and cells infected by viruses. NK cells kill by releasing compounds that cause the target cell to die by a process called apoptosis.

Nestin: Filamentous proteins expressed mostly on nerve cells where they are implicated in the growth of the axon. Nestin is a marker to identify neurons.

Plasticity: Generally means ability to permanently change or transform. In this book it refers to the ability of stem cells to become other types of cells.

Polysaccharide: Relatively complex carbohydrates (complex sugars) made up of many monosaccharides (simple sugars) joined together. They are therefore very large molecules. Common polysaccharides include cellulose (wood), starch and glycogen. Many plant-based polysaccharides have been shown to have health properties.

Semi-permeable membrane: A membrane that allows certain molecules or ions to pass through it while blocking the passage of other molecules or ions.

Senescence: Refers to the biological processes of a living organism approaching an advanced age. When referring to a cell, cellular senescence means the loss of the ability to divide.

Stromal-Derived Factor-1 (SDF-1): SDF-1 is a compound produced by various tissues that attracts stem cells and lymphocytes.

Teratoma: An encapsulated tumor containing various tissue or organ components. For example, a teratoma can contain brain, thyroid, liver, or lung tissues, or even hair, teeth, and bones. At times, a teratoma can even contain more complex organs such as an eyeball, torso, or hand.

REFERENCES

1   Woodbury D, Schwarz EJ, Prockop DJ, and Black IB (2000) Adult Rat and Human Bone Marrow Stromal Cells Differentiate Into Neurons. J. Neurosci Res 61:364–370.

2   Sanchez-Ramos JR (2002) Neural Cells Derived From Adult Bone Marrow and Umbilical Cord Blood. J. Neurosci Res 69:880–893.

3   Jang YY, Collector MI, Baylin SB, Diehl AM, and Sharkis SJ (2004) Hematopoietic stem cells convert into liver cells within days without fusion. Nature Cell Biol. 6(6):532-529.

4   Schwartz RE, Reyes M, Koodie L, Jiang Y, Blackstad M, Lund T, Lenvik T, Johnson S, Hu WS, and Verfaillie CM (2002) Multipotent adult progenitor cells from bone marrow differentiate into functional hepatocyte-like cells. J. Clin. Invest. 109:1291–1302.

5   Amoh, Y., Li, L., Katsuoka, K., and Hoffman, R.M. (2008) Multipotent hair follicle stem cells promote repair of spinal cord injury and recovery of walking function. Cell Cycle 7:1865-1869.

6   Goh ELK, Ma D, Ming GL, and Song H (2003) Adult Neural Stem Cells and Repair of the Adult Central Nervous System. J. Hematotherapy & Stem Cell Research 12:671-679

7   Efrat S. Generation of insulin-producing cells from stem cells for cell replacement therapy of type 1 diabetes. Isr Med Assoc J. 2004 May;6(5):265-7.

8   Kicic A, Shen WY, Wilson AS, Constable IJ, Robertson T, Rakoczy PE. Differentiation of marrow stromal cells

into photoreceptors in the rat eye. J Neurosci. 2003 Aug 27;23(21):7742-9.

9   Orlic D., Kajstura J., Chimenti S. et al. Bone marrow cells regenerate infarcted myocardium. Nature 2001; 410(6829): 701–705.

10 Togel F and Westenfelder C (2007) Adult Bone Marrow–Derived Stem Cells for Organ Regeneration and Repair. Developmental Dynamics 236 (12):3321-31.

11 Bianco P, Riminucci M, Gronthos S, and Robey PG (2001) Bone Marrow Stromal Stem Cells: Nature, Biology, and Potential Applications. Stem Cells 19:180-192.

12 Wang X, Foster M, Al-Dhalimy M, Lagasse E, Finegold M, and Grompe M (2003) The origin and liver repopulating capacity of murine oval cells. PNAS 100(suppl.1):11881-11888.

13 Barker N, van de Wetering M, Clevers H. (2008) The intestinal stem cell. Genes Dev. 22(14):1856-64.

14 Kuang S, Gillespie MA, Rudnicki MA. (2008) Niche regulation of muscle satellite cell self-renewal and differentiation. Cell Stem Cell. 10;2(1):22-31.

15 Revishchin AV, Korochkin LI, Okhotin VE, Pavlova GV. (2008) Neural stem cells in the mammalian brain. Int Rev Cytol. 265:55-109.

16 Burke ZD, Thowfeequ S, Peran M, Tosh D. (2007) Stem cells in the adult pancreas and liver. Biochem J. 404(2):169-78.

17 Díaz-Flores L Jr, Madrid JF, Gutiérrez R, Varela H, Valladares F, Alvarez-Argüelles H, Díaz-Flores L. (2006) Adult stem and transit-amplifying cell location. Histol Histopathol. 21(9):995-1027.

18 Abedi M, Greer DA, Colvin GA, Demers DA, Dooner MS, Harpel JA, Weier HU, Lambert JF, and Quesenberry PJ (2004) Robust conversion of marrow cells to skeletal muscle with formation of marrow-derived muscle colonies: A multifactorial process. *Exp. Hematol.* 32:426-434.

19 Fraser JK, Schreiber RE, Zuk PA, and Hedrick MH (2004) Adult stem cell therapy for the heart. *Intern. J Biochem & Cell Biol* 36:658–666

20 Asahara T, Masuda H, Takahashi T, Kalka C, Pastore C, Silver M, Kearne M, Magner M, and Isner JM (1999) Bone Marrow Origin of Endothelial Progenitor Cells Responsible for Postnatal Vasculogenesis in Physiological and Pathological Neovascularization. *Circ Res.* 85:221-228.

21 Krause DS, Theise ND, Collector MI, Henegariu O, Hwang S, Gardner R, Neutzel S, and Sharkis SJ (2001) Multi-organ, multi-lineage engraftment by a single bone marrow-derived stem cell. *Cell* 105:369-377

22 Branski LK, Gauglitz GG, Herndon DN, and Jeschke MG. (2008) A review of gene and stem cell therapy in cutaneous wound healing. *Burns*, July 4.

23 Dezawa M, Ishikawa H, Hoshino M, Itokazu Y, and Nabeshima Y. (2005) Potential of bone marrow stromal cells in applications for neuro-degenerative, neuro-traumatic and muscle degenerative diseases. *Curr Neuropharmacol.* 3(4):257-66.

24 Rando TA. (2007) The immortal strand hypothesis: segregation and reconstruction. *Cell.* 129(7):1239-43.

25 Jensen GS, Drapeau C. (2002) The use of in situ bone marrow stem cells for the treatment of various degenerative diseases. *Med Hypotheses.* 59(4):422-8.

26 Leone AM, Rutella S, Bonanno G, Contemi AM, de Ritis DG, Giannico MB, Rebuzzi AG, Leone G, Crea F. (2006) Endogenous G-CSF and CD34+ cell mobilization after acute myocardial infarction. *Int J Cardiol.* 111(2):202-8.

27 Abbott JD, Huang Y, Liu D, Hickey R, Krause DS, Giordano FJ. (2004) Stromal cell-derived factor-1alpha plays a critical role in stem cell recruitment to the heart after myocardial infarction but is not sufficient to induce homing in the absence of injury. *Circulation* 110(21):3300-5.

28 Peled A, Grabovsky V, Habler L, Sandbank J, Arenzana-Seisdedos F, Petit I, Ben-Hur H, Lapidot T, Alon R. (1999)

The chemokine SDF-1 stimulates integrin-mediated arrest of CD34(+) cells on vascular endothelium under shear flow. J Clin Invest. 104(9):1199-211.

[29] Vandervelde S, van Luyn MJ, Tio RA, Harmsen MC. (2005) Signaling factors in stem cell-mediated repair of infarcted myocardium. J Mol Cell Cardiol. 39(2):363-76.

[30] Tomoda H, Aoki N. (2003) Bone marrow stimulation and left ventricular function in acute myocardial infarction. Clin Cardiol. 26(10):455-7.

[31] Werner N, Kosiol S, Schiegl T, Ahlers P, Walenta K, Link A, Böhm M, Nickenig G. (2005) Circulating endothelial progenitor cells and cardiovascular outcomes. N Engl J Med. 353(10):999-1007.

[32] Pugh N and Pasco DS. (2001) Characterization of human monocyte activation by a water soluble preparation of *Aphanizomenon flos-aquae*. Phytomedicine 8(6):445-53.

[33] Jensen GS, Ginsberg DI, Huerta P, Citton M, and Drapeau C. (2000) Consumption of *Aphanizomenon flos-aquae* has rapid effects on the circulation and function of immune cells in humans. JANA 2(3):50-58.

[34] Hart A, Zaske LA, Patterson KM, Drapeau C, and Jensen GS (2007) Natural Killer Cell Activation and Modulation of Chemokine Receptor Profile. *In Vitro* by an Extract from the Cyanophyta *Aphanizomenon flos-aquae*. *J Med Food* 10(3): 435–441

[35] Benedetti S, Benvenuti F, Pagliarani S, Francogli S, Scoglio S, Canestrari F. (2004) Antioxidant properties of a novel phycocyanin extract from the blue-green alga *Aphanizomenon flos-aquae*. *Life Sciences* 75(19):2353-2362.

[36] Reddy CM, Bhat VB, Kiranmai G, Reddy MN, Reddanna P, Madyastha KM (2000) Selective inhibition of cyclooxygenase-2 by C-phycocyanin, a biliprotein from Spirulina platensis. *Biochem Biophys Res Commun* 277(3): 599-603.

[37] Romay C, Ledon N, and Gonzalez R. (1999) Phycocyanin extract reduces leukotriene B4 levels in arachidonic acid-

induced mouse-ear inflammation test. *J Pharm Pharmacol* 51(5):641-642.

[38] Sandler M, Ruthven CR, Goodwin BL, Coppen A. (1979) Decreased cerebrospinal fluid concentration of free phenylacetic acid in depressive illness. Clin Chim Acta 93(1):169-71

[39] Baker et al. (1991) Phenylethylaminergic mechanisms in attention-deficit disorder. *Biol Psychiatry* 1991 Jan 1;29(1):15-22

[40] Frenette PS and Weiss L. Sulfated glycans induce rapid hematopoietic progenitor cell mobilization: evidence for selectin-dependent and independent mechanisms. Blood, Vol 96, No 7, pp. 2460-8, 2000

[41] Cottler-Fox MH, Lapidot T, Petit I, Kollet O, DiPersio JF, Link D, Devine S. (2003) Stem cell mobilization. Hematology Am Soc Hematol Educ Program. 419-437.

[42] Jensen GS, Hart AN, Zaske LAM, Drapeau C, Schaeffer DJ and Cruickshank JA. (2007) Mobilization of human CD34+CD133+ and CD34+CD133- stem cells in vivo by consumption of an extract from *Aphanizomenon flos-aquae* - related to modulation of CXCR4 expression by an L-selectin ligand. *Cardiovascular Revascularization Medicine*, 8(3):189-202.

[43] Zhao M, Momma S, Delfani K, Carlen M, Cassidy RM, Johansson CB, Brismar H, Shupliakov O, Frisen J, Janson AM. (2003) Evidence for neurogenesis in the adult mammalian substantia nigra. PNAS 100(13):7925-30.

[44] Carreras E, Saiz A, Marín P, Martínez C, Rovira M, Villamor N, Aymerich M, Lozano M, Fernández-Avilés F, Urbano-Izpizua A, Montserrat E, Graus F. (2003) CD34+ selected autologous peripheral blood stem cell transplantation for multiple sclerosis: report of toxicity and treatment results at one year of follow-up in 15 patients. Haematologica 88(3):306-14.

[45] Ferrari G, Cusella-De Angelis G, Coletta M, Paolucci E, Stornaiuolo A, Cossu G, Mavilio F. (1998) Muscle regeneration

by bone marrow-derived myogenic progenitors. Science 279(5356):1528-30.

46 Tomita M, Adachi Y, Yamada H, Takahashi K, Kiuchi K, Oyaizu H, Ikebukuro K, Kaneda H, Matsumura M, Ikehara S. (2002) Bone marrow-derived stem cells can differentiate into retinal cells in injured rat retina. Stem Cells 20(4):279-83.

47 Kawada H, Takizawa S, Takanashi T, Morita Y, Fujita J, Fukuda K, Takagi S, Okano H, Ando K, Hotta T. (2006) Administration of hematopoietic cytokines in the subacute phase after cerebral infarction is effective for functional recovery facilitating proliferation of intrinsic neural stem/ progenitor cells and transition of bone marrow-derived neuronal cells. Circulation 113(5):701-10.

48 Ince H, Petzsch M, Kleine HD, Schmidt H, Rehders T, Körber T, Schümichen C, Freund M, Nienaber CA. (2005) Preservation from left ventricular remodeling by front-integrated revascularization and stem cell liberation in evolving acute myocardial infarction by use of granulocyte-colony-stimulating factor (FIRSTLINE-AMI). Circulation 112(20):3097-106.

49 Orlic D, Hill JM, Arai AE. (2002) Stem cells for myocardial regeneration. Circ Res. 91(12):1092-102.

50 Orlic D, Kajstura J, Chimenti S, Limana F, Jakoniuk I, Quaini F, Nadal-Ginard B, Bodine DM, Leri A, Anversa P. (2001) Mobilized bone marrow cells repair the infarcted heart, improving function and survival. PNAS 98(18):10344-9.

51 Kollet O, Shivtiel S, Chen YQ, Suriawinata J, Thung SN, Dabeva MD, Kahn J, Spiegel A, Dar A, Samira S, Goichberg P, Kalinkovich A, Arenzana-Seisdedos F, Nagler A, Hardan I, Revel M, Shafritz DA, Lapidot T. (2003) HGF, SDF-1, and MMP-9 are involved in stress-induced human CD34+ stem cell recruitment to the liver. J Clin Invest. 112(2):160-9.

52 Sun Y, Chen L, Hou XG, Hou WK, Dong JJ, Sun L, Tang KX, Wang B, Song J, Li H, Wang KX. (2007) Differentiation

of bone marrow-derived mesenchymal stem cells from diabetic patients into insulin-producing cells in vitro. Chin Med J (Engl) 120(9):771-6.

53 Ianus A, Holz GG, Theise ND, Hussain MA. (2003) In vivo derivation of glucose-competent pancreatic endocrine cells from bone marrow without evidence of cell fusion. J Clin Invest. 111(6):843-50.

54 Lee RH, Seo MJ, Reger RL, Spees JL, Pulin AA, Olson SD, Prockop DJ. (2006) Multipotent stromal cells from human marrow home to and promote repair of pancreatic islets and renal glomeruli in diabetic NOD/scid mice. PNAS 103(46):17438-43.

55 Herrera MB, Bussolati B, Bruno S, Fonsato V, Romanazzi GM, Camussi G. (2004) Mesenchymal stem cells contribute to the renal repair of acute tubular epithelial injury. Int J Mol Med. 14(6):1035-41.

56 Iwasaki M, Adachi Y, Minamino K, Suzuki Y, Zhang Y, Okigaki M, Nakano K, Koike Y, Wang J, Mukaide H, Taketani S, Mori Y, Takahashi H, Iwasaka T, Ikehara S. (2005) Mobilization of bone marrow cells by G-CSF rescues mice from cisplatin-induced renal failure, and M-CSF enhances the effects of G-CSF. J Am Soc Nephrol. 16(3):658-66.

57 Rojas M, Xu J, Woods CR, Mora AL, Spears W, Roman J, Brigham KL. (2005) Bone marrow-derived mesenchymal stem cells in repair of the injured lung. Am J Respir Cell Mol Biol. 33(2):145-52.

58 Yamada M, Kubo H, Kobayashi S, Ishizawa K, Numasaki M, Ueda S, Suzuki T, Sasaki H. (2004) Bone marrow-derived progenitor cells are important for lung repair after lipopolysaccharide-induced lung injury. J Immunol. 172(2):1266-72.

59 Mansilla E, Marín GH, Drago H, Sturla F, Salas E, Gardiner C, Bossi S, Lamonega R, Guzmán A, Nuñez A, Gil MA, Piccinelli G, Ibar R, Soratti C. (2006) Bloodstream cells phenotypically identical to human mesenchymal bone

marrow stem cells circulate in large amounts under the influence of acute large skin damage: new evidence for their use in regenerative medicine. Transplant Proc. 38(3):967-9.

[60] Borue X, Lee S, Grove J, Herzog EL, Harris R, Diflo T, Glusac E, Hyman K, Theise ND, Krause DS. (2004) Bone marrow-derived cells contribute to epithelial engraftment during wound healing. Am J Pathol. 165(5):1767-72.

[61] Bozlar M, Aslan B, Kalaci A, Baktiroglu L, Yanat AN, Tasci A. (2005) Effects of human granulocyte-colony stimulating factor on fracture healing in rats. Saudi Med J. 26(8):1250-4.

[62] Burt RK, Oyama Y, Verda L, Quigley K, Brush M, Yaung K, Statkute L, Traynor A, Barr WG. (2004) Induction of remission of severe and refractory rheumatoid arthritis by allogeneic mixed chimerism. Arthritis Rheum. 50(8):2466-70.